KS2 English

SAT Buster

Punctuation

Book 2

Here's what you have to do...

In Year 6 you have to take some tests called the SATs.
This book will help you do well in the punctuation bit of the tests.

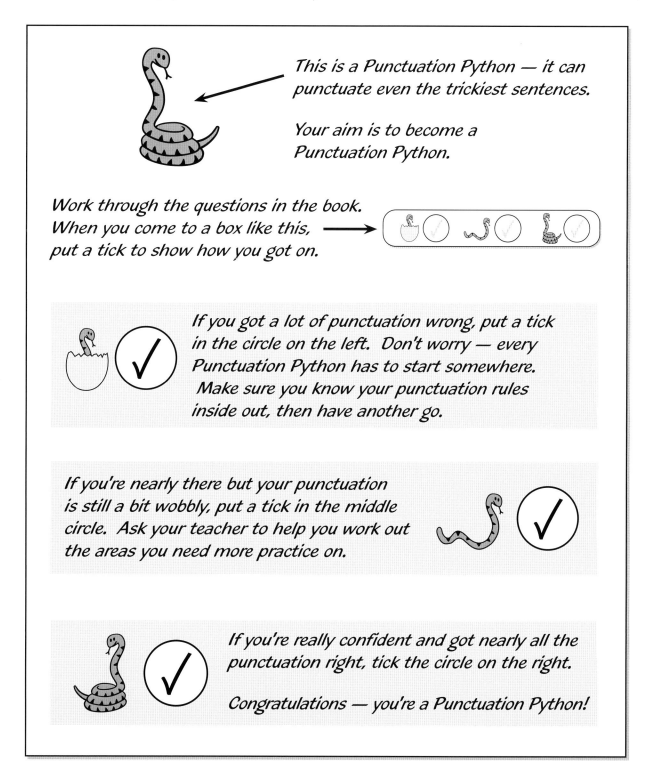

This is a Punctuation Python — it can
punctuate even the trickiest sentences.

Your aim is to become a
Punctuation Python.

Work through the questions in the book.
When you come to a box like this,
put a tick to show how you got on.

If you got a lot of punctuation wrong, put a tick
in the circle on the left. Don't worry — every
Punctuation Python has to start somewhere.
Make sure you know your punctuation rules
inside out, then have another go.

If you're nearly there but your punctuation
is still a bit wobbly, put a tick in the middle
circle. Ask your teacher to help you work out
the areas you need more practice on.

If you're really confident and got nearly all the
punctuation right, tick the circle on the right.

Congratulations — you're a Punctuation Python!

It's another Quality Book from CGP

This is Book 2 in our KS2 SAT Buster range for Punctuation. It's full of tricky questions to help pupils prepare for the Year 6 SATs.

(The difficulty level is the same as Book 1, so it's perfect for extra punctuation practice — or you can use this book on its own.)

Children can use the Punctuation Python tick boxes for self-assessment, which helps you work out how they're getting on.

What CGP is all about

Our sole aim here at CGP is to produce the highest quality books — carefully written, immaculately presented and dangerously close to being funny.

Then we work our socks off to get them out to you — at the cheapest possible prices.

Punctuation Hints and Tips

The tips on this page may come in handy if you're having a punctuation problem.

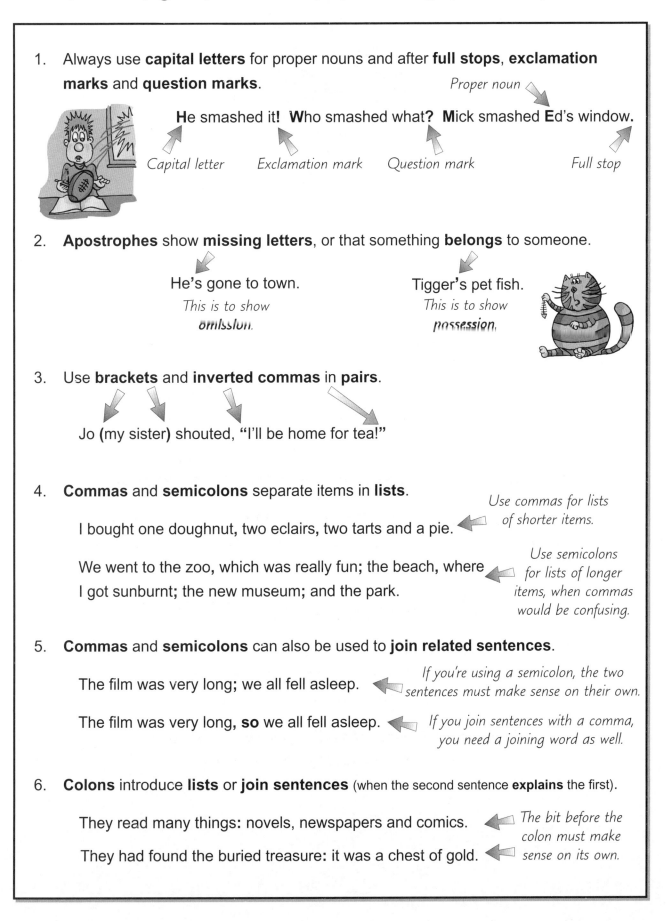

1. Always use **capital letters** for proper nouns and after **full stops**, **exclamation marks** and **question marks**.

   Proper noun

   He smashed it! **W**ho smashed what? **M**ick smashed **E**d's window.

   Capital letter   *Exclamation mark*   *Question mark*   *Full stop*

2. **Apostrophes** show **missing letters**, or that something **belongs** to someone.

   He's gone to town.
   This is to show omission.

   Tigger's pet fish.
   This is to show possession.

3. Use **brackets** and **inverted commas** in **pairs**.

   Jo **(**my sister**)** shouted, **"**I'll be home for tea!**"**

4. **Commas** and **semicolons** separate items in **lists**.

   I bought one doughnut, two eclairs, two tarts and a pie. ← *Use commas for lists of shorter items.*

   We went to the zoo, which was really fun; the beach, where I got sunburnt; the new museum; and the park. ← *Use semicolons for lists of longer items, when commas would be confusing.*

5. **Commas** and **semicolons** can also be used to **join related sentences**.

   The film was very long; we all fell asleep. ← *If you're using a semicolon, the two sentences must make sense on their own.*

   The film was very long, **so** we all fell asleep. ← *If you join sentences with a comma, you need a joining word as well.*

6. **Colons** introduce **lists** or **join sentences** (when the second sentence **explains** the first).

   They read many things: novels, newspapers and comics. ← *The bit before the colon must make sense on its own.*

   They had found the buried treasure: it was a chest of gold. ←

Contents

Published by CGP

Editors
Emma Bonney, Lucy Loveluck, Heather McClelland, Holly Poynton, Sabrina Robinson, Matt Topping
With thanks to Glenn Rogers for the proofreading.

ISBN: 978 1 78294 277 1

www.cgpbooks.co.uk
Clipart from Corel®
Printed by Elanders Ltd, Newcastle upon Tyne.
Based on the classic CGP style created by Richard Parsons.

Section 1 — Basic Punctuation

Capital Letters and Full Stops

Capital letters are quick — they come first. Full stops are slow — they come last. Let's race!

1. Here are some statements about when you should use capital letters.
    Put a tick after the ones that are correct.

    At the start of a new sentence ☐

    For all nouns and pronouns ☐

    For countries and cities ☐

    At the start of a new paragraph ☐

    For all verbs and adjectives ☐

    For people's names ☐

2. Circle the letters in the sentences below that should be capital letters.

    a. i don't think february is a very nice month — it's usually dark and rainy.

    b. he's travelling to poland on tuesday to visit his sister.

    c. roger gave angela a bouquet of flowers for her birthday.

    d. they hoped that michael would enjoy his new job in paris.

3. Rewrite these sentences with capital letters and full stops in the correct places.

    a. **the car slowly turned into market street**

    ....

    b. **there was some fish in hayley's fridge**

    ....

    c. **John and i are Working in birmingham**

    ....

Capital Letters and Full Stops

4. Use all the words in the boxes below to write a sentence.
    Add capital letters and full stops where they are needed.

last   to   london   monday   eileen   moved

    ....

5. Use the words in the box to complete the passage below.
    Add capital letters where they are needed.

    foot   spain   dr clarke   sport   pony   wednesday

On ...., Ruby went to see .... about her sore

.... It had started to hurt last week when her pet, a very chubby

..............................., had stood on it. The doctor told Ruby to rest and to stop playing

.... for a while. Ruby hoped it would get better soon because she

was going on holiday to .... next week.

6. Write a sentence using each of the words below.
    Add capital letters and full stops where they are needed.

    a. england: ....

    b. sunday: ....

    c. naomi: ....

    d. mainsgate road: ....

Punctuation Pythons never forget to use capital letters and full stops. Do you always remember to use them too?

Exclamation Marks and Question Marks

Full stops aren't the only way to end a sentence. There are other punctuation marks too...

1. Read these sentences. Put a tick next to the sentences with the correct punctuation.

   Do you know what time the library opens! ☐

   Oh no! The library's been burgled! ☐ *Use exclamation marks to show strong emotion or to emphasise a point.*

   I demand that you open the library this instant? ☐

   Where is the library? ☐

   Someone call the fire brigade! The library's on fire! ☐

2. Add an exclamation mark or a question mark to each of the sentences below.

   a. I love lasagne and chips.....   f. Who is that man.....

   b. Don't you dare break it.....   g. Jack won a sports car.....

   c. Can you close the window.....   h. Do they seem happy.....

   d. Stop the car right now.....   i. Get out of my house.....

   e. Have you been to Venice.....   j. How many are there.....

3. Use the words in the boxes below to write three questions.
   Use two words for each question, but only use each word once.

   | man | bus | tiger | spaghetti | seaside | tree |

   1) ....

   2) ....

   3) ....

Exclamation Marks and Question Marks

4. Write an exclamation which includes these words: **shark**   **boat**   **water**

....

Write a question which includes these words: **time**   **shop**   **close**

....

5. Write four sentences on the dotted lines below.
Make sure your sentences end with the punctuation marks shown in the boxes.

.... **!**

.... **?**

.... **!**

.... **?**

6. Circle the punctuation marks that have been used incorrectly in the passage below:

Granny and Grandpa had an argument last night. Granny wanted to watch

'Sternly Go Walking' on TV, but Grandpa wanted to watch 'Game of the Evening'?

"Give me the remote control or your flat cap gets it?" shouted Granny, holding

Grandpa's cap out of the window and threatening to drop it into the pond below.

"Do you think that's going to work!" asked Grandpa. "I've got another ten upstairs."

Granny looked a little disappointed and decided to retreat to the kitchen to

gather her thoughts. How could she get Grandpa to change the channel.

A Punctuation Python can use exclamation marks and question marks in the right places. Can you? Tick a box.

Sentences

Sentences can be statements, questions or commands. They're pretty handy.

1. Draw lines to match each sentence to the correct label below.

Open the box carefully.

How many guests are coming?

Write the answer below.

We'll only win if we work together.

Does anyone like baking?

Question

Statement

Command

2. Circle the sentences below which are commands.

There's a problem.   Go to your room.   Sam sings well.

I don't know.   Give Ian the message.

Take a break.   Do your best.

We told the truth.   Ruth can drive.   Play nicely.

3. Read these sentences and write down whether each one is a command or a statement.

We're going on holiday to Torquay.   ....

Go on holiday to Torquay.   ....

I would go on holiday to Torquay.   ....

Sentences

4. Read each pair of sentences.

    Tick the box next to the version with the most suitable punctuation.

    a. **David likes football.** ☐   **David likes football!** ☐

    b. **How do you feel.** ☐   **How do you feel?** ☐

    c. **Don't make a mess!** ☐   **Don't make a mess?** ☐

    d. **Run, Michael, run.** ☐   **Run, Michael, run!** ☐

    e. **I'm a doctor.** ☐   **I'm a doctor?** ☐

5. Underline the commands in the passage below.

    Ellie and Mavis were decorating the living room. They were having a surprise party

    for Dad. It was all going well until Mum walked in. At the top of her voice, she said,

    "Wow! This looks great! I've never seen so many balloons!"

    "Be quiet!" whispered Ellie. "Dad's upstairs and he mustn't find out about the party."

    "We could use your help though," said Mavis. "Hang these streamers up, please."

    "Then check the cake in the oven," added Ellie. Mum smiled at the girls.

    "I'm happy to help," she said. "Give me the ladders and show me what to do."

    Mum tried to help, but it all went wrong. She ripped the decorations, she almost fell

    off the ladder and she forgot all about the cake. In the end, Mavis said,

    "Leave it to us next time, Mum!"

6. Use the pictures below to write (a) a question and (b) a command on the dotted lines.

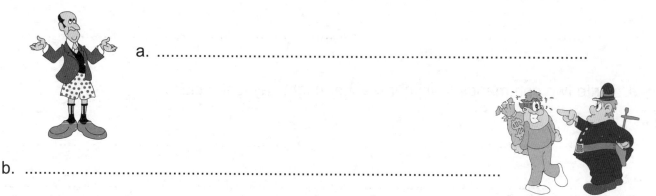

a. ....

b. ....

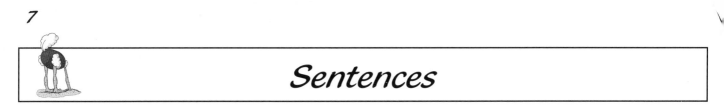

Sentences

7. Use the words in the boxes below to write two 'To Do' lists using commands.
    Only use each word once.

| ~~dog~~ | car | bedroom | dinner | dishwasher | lawn |

To Do
Walk the dog. ....
....
....

To Do
....
....
....

8. Gary wants to find out the following information about Trisha.
    Write down the questions he could ask.

    a. Her favourite animal

        What's your favourite animal? ....

    b. Her age

        ....

    c. Whether she likes dancing

        ....

    d. Where she went on holiday last year

        ....

9. Write two commands that your teacher might say to the class.

    ....

    ....

Sentences

10. Sort the sentences below under the correct heading in the table.

Write either a question mark or an exclamation mark at the end of each sentence.

Grab the runaway chicken   **Where's Jim**

Get out of the way   **Don't do that**   **Have you been away**

Can you dance

Command	Question
....	....
....	....
....	....

11. Put an 'S' in each box after a statement, a 'C' in each box after a command and a 'Q' in each box after a question.

a. I'm really cold ☐

b. Forget about your worries ☐

c. Edgar works at the quarry ☐

d. Tuck your shirt in ☐

e. He collects puppets ☐

f. Can you play tennis ☐

g. Tell Mrs Preston the truth ☐

h. Do you eat fish ☐

i. My ankle is swollen ☐

j. Write your name at the top ☐

Questions and commands don't cause any problems for Punctuation Pythons. Do you feel confident about them too?

Mixed Practice

Let's take a look back at section 1 with this mixed bag of questions.

1. Read these sentences and write down whether each one is a question or a statement.

    Do you prefer white chocolate or milk chocolate?   ....

    Fran always has a good supply of chocolate.   ....

2. Read these sentences. Tick the box next to the
    sentence which uses capital letters correctly.

    a. **Next Tuesday, Mr Morrison is going on Holiday to New Zealand.** ☐

    b. **Next tuesday, mr Morrison is going on holiday to New Zualand.** ☐

    c. **Next Tuesday, Mr Morrison is going on holiday to New Zealand.** ☐

3. Draw a line to match each of these sentences to the correct punctuation mark.

?		
	Watch out	**Who is it**
I feel on top of the world		**How did you do it**
That's great news	**I'm telling you to stop it**	
What's going on	**Don't annoy him**	!

4. The words in this sentence are all jumbled up. Rewrite the sentence in the
    correct order and add capital letters and a full stop where they are needed.

in	italy	is	thursday	karl	playing	on	golf

    ....

Mixed Practice

5. Write a possible question to match each answer below. Use the correct punctuation.

I found a treasure map.   *What did you find?*

It's the smell of seaweed.   ....

We made a mess.   ....

He can play the piano.   ....

6. Put an 'S' in each box after a statement, and a 'C' in each box after a command.

a. Sam loves cherry jam.   ☐   e. Call me when you get home.   ☐

b. Change your shirt.   ☐   f. The children are playing.   ☐

c. We are a rock band.   ☐   g. Do your homework.   ☐

d. Edgar lives in Exeter.   ☐   h. Pass me the butter.   ☐

7. Look at this sentence.

Come out with your hands up!

Why has an exclamation mark been used?

....

....

That's the first section completed! Are you becoming more like a Punctuation Python? Tick the box to show your level.

Apostrophes

Apostrophes can show that words have been combined to form a contraction.

1. Circle all the **contractions** in the box below.

    A contraction is a shortened version of a phrase.

    > can't   verb   we have   they're
    >
    > there's   I'm
    >
    > doesn't
    >
    > his   carrot   can

2. Rewrite the words below as **contractions**.

    she is ➡ ......she's......   **was not** ➡ ....

    we had ➡ ....   **who is** ➡ ....

    you are ➡ ....   **could not** ➡ ....

    they have ➡ ....   **she had** ➡ ....

    he has ➡ ....   **would have** ➡ ....

3. Tick the sentences which use apostrophes correctly.

    a. Cara won't call me until she's ready. ☐

    b. The girls migh'tve stayed longer if it had rained. ☐

    c. She'd forgotten how to use her toothbrush. ☐

    d. Brendan isn't happy with the result. ☐

    e. She hadnt' handed in her homework. ☐

    f. They were'nt impressed by the duck's performance. ☐

Apostrophes

4. Circle the correct version of each word in the sentences below.

    Florence's / Florences bedroom was in the dungeon.

    We ate the **farme'rs / farmer's** sandwiches by mistake.

    Emilys' / Emily's sock had a gigantic hole in the heel.

Apostrophes can also show when something belongs to someone.

5. Each of these sentences is missing an apostrophe.
    Tick the box above where the apostrophe should be added.

    ☐   ☐   ☐

    Stephens friend, Mike, has lots of colouring books.

    ☐   ☐   ☐

    The balloons we found on the stairs were Margarets.

    ☐   ☐   ☐

    Thomas and Joel bought the elephants favourite doughnuts.

6. Complete these sentences by writing out the word in brackets to show possession.

    Elspeth shook .... (Michael) hand vigorously before the meeting.

    The .... (company) president forgot to wear any trousers.

    We couldn't find the .... (children) party anywhere.

    It was difficult to see how the .... (sheep) food had just disappeared.

    The .... (tree) branches were blown about by the wind.

Section 2 — Apostrophes and Inverted Commas

Apostrophes

7. Write out each of the sentences below using apostrophes.

   The badger that belongs to the boy. ⟹ *The boy's badger.* ....

   The badger that belongs to the boys. ⟹ ....

   The badgers that belong to the boys. ⟹ ....

8. Put a tick next to the sentences where the word in bold is **plural**.

   'Plural' means more than one.

   A plane landed in the **cows'** field. ☑

   Ellie hasn't met her **brothers'** friends. ☐

   I didn't see the **crocodile's** tail. ☐

   The **ladies'** hats were all bright green. ☐

   Hugh didn't like the **book's** cover. ☐

9. Rewrite these sentences with apostrophes in the correct places.

   Lolas treehouse has got two trapdoors.

   ....

   Garys parrots are very colourful.

   ....

   The womens dresses were really beautiful.

   ....

   Gareths jumper was knitted by Brians uncle.

   ....

Apostrophes

10. Draw a line to match each sentence with the correct form of **its** or **it's**.

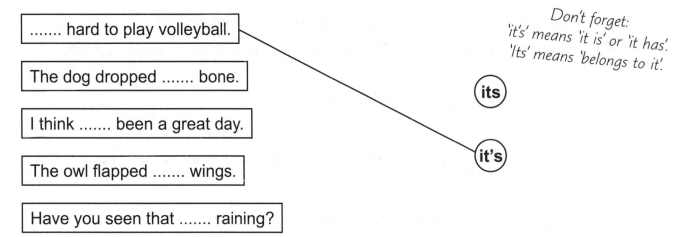

.... hard to play volleyball.

The dog dropped .... bone.

I think .... been a great day.

The owl flapped .... wings.

Have you seen that .... raining?

Don't forget:
'it's' means 'it is' or 'it has'.
'Its' means 'belongs to it'.

its

it's

11 Cross out the incorrect word in each sentence.

We think that **they're / their** trying to steal our muffins.

Don't be late or you'll miss **you're / your** favourite programme.

Did you know that **we're / were** going to be in a film?

You're / Your going to have to run faster than that to win the race.

There / They're is the bike that you were going to buy.

12. Write a sentence which uses all of the words in the box correctly.

| it's | you're | we're |

....

....

Punctuation Pythons are amazing at apostrophes.
Are you feeling as proud as a python?

Section 2 — Apostrophes and Inverted Commas

Inverted Commas

Inverted commas are also known as speech marks — they show that someone's speaking.

1. Each of these sentences needs a set of inverted commas adding.
   Put them into the correct boxes. The first set has already been added for you.

   "I can't hear anything! $\boxed{"}$ she exclaimed. $\boxed{}$

   Suzie $\boxed{}$ explained, $\boxed{}$ You need to boil the sprouts before you eat them."

   $\boxed{}$ Alan speaks $\boxed{}$ so slowly," said Daniela.

   $\boxed{}$ I asked the penguin, $\boxed{}$ Do you know where the hospital is?"

2. Rewrite the sentences below, adding inverted commas in the right places.

   Tim said, I'm really cold. ➡ ....

   Catch that frog! I cried. ➡ ....

   What's for tea? asked Vic. ➡ ....

3. Tick the sentences which contain **direct speech**.

   I heard Phil say that Siân was very happy. $\boxed{}$

   The train only stopped at two stations. $\boxed{}$

   Alex shouted, "Can you come here please!" $\boxed{}$

   Elliot was confused; Martin was angry. $\boxed{}$

   "We've got a long journey ahead of us," said Ian. $\boxed{}$

Inverted Commas

4. Draw lines to match these sentences with the correct type of speech.

| Always uses inverted commas. |

| Never uses inverted commas. |

| Summarises what someone says. |

| Is exactly what someone says. |

| direct speech |

| reported speech |

5. These sentences are all in reported speech.
    Rewrite them so that they are in **direct speech**.

Don't forget to use a capital letter at the start of direct speech.

Stephen said that the film was dreadful.

Stephen said, "The film was dreadful."

We said that there were too many people at the park.

....

Esther asked if Ruth can go shopping on Monday.

....

I said that we should make a chocolate house.

....

6. Use the words below to write a sentence using **direct speech**.

socks   **tennis**

....

uncle   **cheesecake**

....

Inverted Commas

7. Read each sentence and tick the correct box to show if it is **direct** or **reported speech**.

direct   reported

Fara said that James was a brilliant poet. ☐ ☐

"Alistair is a clever man," said the professor. ☐ ☐

"We have to find that coin!" exclaimed Martha. ☐ ☐

Zosia asked whether the bear was real. ☐ ☐

8. Rewrite the sentences below using **reported speech**.

"Can you see the Moon?" asked Brian.

....

Glenda said, "Tracy can't play hockey tonight."

....

Tony shouted, "There's a bull in the garden!"

....

9. Choose **one** of the topics from the box and write two
    sentences about it using **reported speech**.

music   hamsters

swimming   golf

....

....

....

....

Inverted Commas

10. Use your own words to fill in the gaps in the conversation between Charlie and Tom.
    Then write out the conversation on the lines below using **reported speech**.

    Charlie: "Tom, how was .... yesterday?"

    Tom: "It was ...., thanks."

    Charlie: "Did you see..there?"

    Tom: "No, ..."

    ....

    ....

    ....

    ....

11. Read the paragraph below. Rewrite it, changing the **direct speech** to **reported speech**.

    > Frank said, "The tower is far too tall to climb."
    > Arthur said, "I like a challenge."
    > Arthur's mum said, "Challenges aren't always a good thing."
    > Frank said, "Maybe we should climb the stairs instead."

    ....

    ....

    ....

    ....

*Punctuation Pythons can sssssslip inverted commas into
the right places. Are your sssssentences looking good too?*

Section 2 — Apostrophes and Inverted Commas

Mixed Practice

Ready to test your apostrophe and inverted comma skills? Here's a mix of questions for you.

1. This sentence is missing **three** bits of punctuation. Write them in the boxes.

   ☐ **Those are the girls** ☐ **bags!** ☐ **shouted Rani.**

2. Complete the table below.

Full words	Contraction
I am	
	you're
they had	
	we're

3. Rewrite this sentence using direct speech.

   Sophia shouted that there are no biscuits left in the tin.

   ....

4. Complete these sentences using the contracted forms of the words in brackets.

   The bear .... (would not) stop hugging the tree.

   We .... (might have) been on time if you had got out of bed.

   Emily said that .... (she has) found the right house.

   ".............................. (we are) ready to go to Jupiter," said the children.

   Charles .... (should have) remembered to bring his crown.

Mixed Practice

5. Read the paragraph below, then write down on the lines which characters use reported speech and which use direct speech.

> **Ian called that it was time to go.**
> **Dawn replied, "I'm not quite ready. Can you wait for a minute or two?"**
> **Emma added, "I'm going to be about five minutes." Joanna was cross**
> **and said that she was going to go on her own.**
> **Grandad whispered, "Joanna, can I come with you?"**

reported speech ➡ ....*Ian*........... ....

direct speech ➡ ....

6. Draw lines to match up the phrases which mean the same thing.

the baker's cakes		several cakes belonging to several bakers
the bakers' cakes		several cakes belonging to the baker

7. There are **two** punctuation mistakes in each of these sentences.
    Rewrite them correctly on the lines.

"Have you eaten Harriets' hairbrush? enquired Sara.

....

Its too difficult!" shouted Millie.

....

"Were very close" to their house, said Paul.

....

Hooray — you've slithered your way to the end of the section!
Tick a box to show how well you think you've done.

Section 2 — Apostrophes and Inverted Commas

Commas

Commas are very common, so it's important to know how to use them correctly.

1. Each sentence below is missing one comma. Put a comma in the correct place.

   I know how to make fudge peppermint creams and chocolate mice.

   Ralph Tom and Bertha were all working on the fruit and vegetables stall.

   The exhibition had dinosaur bones from America Argentina and Chile.

2. For each sentence below, write in the box how many commas should be added. The first one has been done for you.

   a. I have a clarinet lesson and a football match today. | 0 |

   b. The four seasons are spring summer autumn and winter.

   c. My brothers are aged seven twelve and fourteen.

   d. Zoe Azra Lily and Omar have all been to Turkey this year.

   e. We took photos and video recordings in the forest.

3. Only one of these commas is needed. Circle the two commas that aren't needed.

   The firework display had, rockets, Catherine wheels, and Roman candles.

Summer Fair

Saturday 5th July

Pony rides carousel and candyfloss.

Fun for all the family!

10am-4pm
Parish church

4. There's a comma missing from this poster. Rewrite the part of the text that's wrong, with a comma in the right place.

   ....

   ....

Commas

5. Here are some sentences about commas. Put a circle around the ones that are true.

> **A comma can be used with a conjunction to join two main clauses.**
>
> **Commas can be used to join subordinate and main clauses.**
>
> **Commas can be be used instead of inverted commas.**
>
> **Commas can be used at the end of a sentence.**
>
> **Commas can be used to separate items in a list.**

6. Each of these sentences is missing a comma. Put a comma in one of the boxes to make each sentence correct.

Before ☐ you climb the wall ☐ make sure that ☐ your safety line is tight.

Mrs Jennings, who is ☐ our next-door neighbour ☐ baked us ☐ a cake.

7. Write a sentence using the clauses in the boxes and **two** commas.

| who seemed very familiar | got off at the wrong stop | the man on the bus |

....

....

8. Write something in each gap to complete the sentence.

a. Our fire station, ..., needs volunteers.

b. Captain Rogers, ..., shaved his beard.

c. Hanz and Jonas, ..., are staying here.

Section 3 — Commas, Hyphens, Brackets and Dashes

Commas

9. Read this sentence.

> **While his mum fried the onions, Oliver cooked the burgers.**

Why is the comma used?

....

....

10. Rewrite these sentences so that the commas are in the correct places.

At eight o'clock this morning I, started studying.

....

As I stepped, into the aeroplane I felt really nervous.

....

With a deep breath Luke reached for, the tarantula.

....

11. Tick the box next to the sentences that are punctuated correctly.

As long as the first domino falls over properly, the rest should follow. ☐

As well as swimming my sister goes to four after-school clubs. ☐

The band's new single, which was released last week, is already very popular. ☐

Although I like doughnuts I think they smell horrible. ☐

When her old mug smashed, Rebecca had to buy a new one. ☐

Commas

12. Put a tick in the boxes to show where commas are needed in this passage.

Wherever Laura goes Naomi always follows. They do karate club tennis lessons

⬆ ⬜   ⬆ ⬜   ⬆ ⬜   ⬆ ⬜

and sewing club together. During the holidays they often stay at each other's houses.

⬆ ⬜   ⬆ ⬜   ⬆ ⬜

13. Rewrite this paragraph with the commas in the correct places. All the commas you need are already in the paragraph — they are just in the wrong places.

From the outside the fortress looked, completely sealed. We could see archers on every turret a portcullis, across the door and a frozen moat — our chances of success were small. We crept towards the north, side which felt slightly safer and planned, our next move carefully.

....

....

....

....

....

....

....

Have you conquered your commas? If so, you're well on the way to becoming a Punctuation Python. Tick, tick away...

Hyphens

Hyphens bring together two words, or two parts of a word.

1. Draw lines to match each phrase with the correct definition.

| my great grandfather | a cleaning room that is dry |

| a dry-cleaning room | my father's grandfather |

| a dry cleaning-room | a room for dry-cleaning |

| my great-grandfather | my grandfather, who is great |

2. Underline the correct word to complete each sentence below.

   The superhero took some time to (**re-lax / relax**) after saving the world again.

   The dog (**re-treated / retreated**) to his kennel when it began to snow.

   Margery wanted to (**re-lay / relay**) her carpet after the floods.

   Jimmy (**re-acted / reacted**) badly when I told him the computer was broken.

   The supermarket still hasn't (**re-plied / replied**) to my letter about the mouldy bread.

3. Only one of the hyphens is needed in each of these sentences.
   Cross out all of the hyphens that aren't needed.

   The house next door has huge-rooms with leather-covered sofas.

   Gina's half-finished-project was lying upside down on the kitchen-floor.

   The cream-filled cupcakes were iced-lightly and had chocolate-sprinkles.

Hyphens

4. Tick the version of each sentence which uses hyphens correctly.

a. Ivy was re-elected as president. ☐   Ivy was reelected as president. ☐

b. Rob said to re-fresh the page. ☐   Rob said to refresh the page. ☐

c. Sonja re-signed for the parcel. ☐   Sonja resigned for the parcel. ☐

d. I couldn't re-member the lyrics. ☐   I couldn't remember the lyrics. ☐

5. Each sentence below is missing one hyphen.
Rewrite each sentence with the hyphen in the correct place.

There are thirty six aliens repairing the rocket.

....

Uncle Fred chose the orange flavoured ice cream.

....

6. Some of these sentences are missing a hyphen. Add hyphens where they are needed.
Some of the sentences might be correct already.

The annual elephant race is taking place this weekend.

Living in the garden was only a short term solution.

Petra was feeling tired , bored and under appreciated.

Jenny has got a new part time job at the supermarket.

My brother's ex girlfriend has moved in down the road.

*Do you need to re-cover these pages, or are you as handy
with hyphens as a Punctuation Python? Time to tick a box.*

Section 3 — Commas, Hyphens, Brackets and Dashes

Brackets

Brackets are used to separate off extra information (like dates) in a sentence.

1. Rewrite each sentence, and use a pair of brackets to add the words in the box in the right place. The first one has been done for you.

Mr Martin is very strict.   **my maths teacher**

Mr Martin (my maths teacher) is very strict.
....

Everdew Road is blocked off today.   **our street**

....

Rosie's present was for her horse.   **a new saddle**

....

2. The box below contains a sentence that's been jumbled up.
Draw a line from the beginning of the sentence to the end,
going through the punctuation marks in the right places.

(were on special offer   )

.

My favourite flavour crisps   **tuna and tomato ketchup**

3. Write something in the gaps between the brackets to complete these sentences.

The weather today (...) is quite surprising.

Velma's new puppy (...) has caused chaos.

The magician's trick (...) amazed us all.

All of the zoo's animals (...) are being moved.

Brackets

4. This paragraph is missing some brackets. Fix the paragraph by putting brackets in the correct boxes.

Phil caught ☐ his train ☐ the 6:01 ☐ just in time. All of the carriages

☐ five in total ☐ were already overcrowded ☐ , so he couldn't get a seat.

Phil squeezed himself ☐ between the luggage racks ☐ and a man who was

reading a newspaper ☐ the Daily Shout ☐ , and breathed a sigh of relief.

5. Write a sentence using these words and a pair of brackets.

my wouldn't at upstairs nine bedtime go sister o'clock

....

....

6. Tick the sentences where brackets have been used correctly.

We found the beavers' dam (a metre wide just downstream. ☐

The first competition (ice-skating) started at midday. ☐

(PC Oliver) chased the criminal over the bridge and under the hedge. ☐

The whole wolf pack (one hundred strong) let out a howl. ☐

Dion is useless in the mornings (unless she's eaten pancakes). ☐

Are you a whizz at brackets (like a Punctuation Python) or do you still find them tricky? Tick a box and let's see.

Dashes and Bullet Points

Dashes are a great punctuation mark to master — they'll make your writing really smashing.

1. Write your own sentence using the phrases in the boxes and **two** dashes.

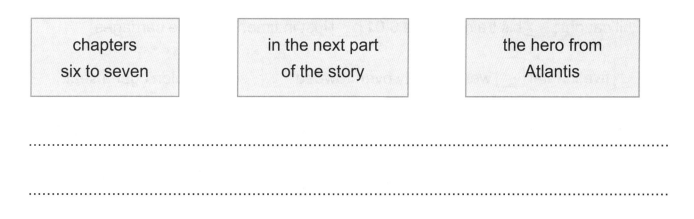

| chapters six to seven | in the next part of the story | the hero from Atlantis |

....

....

2. Add **two** dashes to each of these sentences so that they are punctuated correctly.

The local supermarket Purse Buster is organising a fun run.

An old couple I think they were tourists asked me for help.

Queen Victoria born in 1819 ruled Britain for sixty-three years.

Our science club which meets on Tuesdays is buying a gecko.

3. Put a tick in **one** box for each sentence below, to show where the dash is needed.

No one could hear what Artem was saying he was practically whispering.

My friend Thomas always eats honey sandwiches his mum is a beekeeper.

I have three best friends at school Elia, Matthew and Josephine.

Dashes and Bullet Points

4. Sort the sentences into the table on the right. The first one has been done for you.

   a. Harry my pet tortoise is always hungry.

   b. I'm wearing two jumpers it's freezing.

   c. Get help the cookies are exploding!

   d. The knight a big man put on his armour.

Needs one dash	Needs two dashes
	a

5. Only some of these dashes are needed. Cross out all the dashes that aren't needed.

   I tried — to get rid of the fly — it was annoying me — but it wouldn't — leave.

   Dad — is building — my birthday present in — the basement — it's a secret.

   I ran five — circuits of the track — that's two kilometres — in ten — minutes.

   Marcus decided — he had to buy — the shoes — they were — a perfect fit.

6. Here is a list of jobs Miss Jennings has left for her class to complete.
   Write out the list using bullet points.

   Today you need to do these things: finish your essays on King Arthur, start researching your nature projects and tidy your desks ready for the weekend.

   Today you need to do these things:

   ....

   ....

   ....

Punctuation Pythons think dashes and bullet points are delicious, especially with eggs. How do you find them?

Section 3 — Commas, Hyphens, Brackets and Dashes

Mixed Practice

Let's unite all that punctuation into one big, happy family (brackets are the grandparents).

1. Draw lines to match these descriptions to the correct punctuation mark.

Can be used to separate lists, or to join clauses in a sentence.	dashes
Can join together two words, or two parts of a word.	bullet points
Can add extra information to a sentence, alone or in pairs.	commas
Always come in pairs to add extra information to a sentence.	brackets
Can be used to display information in a vertical list.	hyphens

2. Write whether a hyphen or a dash should complete each sentence below.
    The first one has been done for you.

    You shouldn't swim in shark ... infested waters. ....*hyphen*............

    This sandwich is awful ... there's sand in it. ....

    I speak two languages ... English and Spanish. ....

    Lianne's going on an all ... inclusive trip to Benidorm. ....

3. Rewrite this sentence, adding in dashes where they are needed.

    My rabbits Pippin and Tash are having babies.

    ....

Mixed Practice

4. Rewrite these sentences using commas.

   Nim got dressed ate breakfast and brushed his teeth.

   ....

   Courtney the first dancer wasn't feeling confident.

   ....

   Joel likes watching rugby yet he can't play it.

   ....

5. Read these sentences. Put a tick in the box next to the sentences which are correct.
   Then circle the punctuation error in each incorrect sentence.

   a. **Violet was very confused — the soup had turned blue.** ☐

   b. **Pedro, Chris and Carrie, went to Manchester last week.** ☐

   c. **I couldn't re-call where I'd left my science project.** ☐

   d. **Bradley and Drew — my twin brothers — are twelve today.** ☐

   e. **Mr Atkinson (a local farmer has bought) our spare field.** ☐

   f. **These new lightly-salted crisps are absolutely delicious.** ☐

6. This sentence is missing some words. Add words of your own so that the sentence
   makes sense and is punctuated correctly.

   Gillington Singers, ... **,**

   rehearse on .... **,** .... **and** .... **evenings.**

Mixed Practice

7. These sentences are missing some punctuation marks. Add the correct punctuation mark to the correct box. Some boxes don't need a punctuation mark.

   a. That's ☐ Geronimo (next door's dog ☐ running down ☐ the street.

   b. Henry ☐ Juan ☐ and I go to St. Mark's ☐ a school in the next town.

   c. Santa had to re☐sort all the letters after the reindeers ☐ got hold of them.

   d. Although ☐ jelly juggling is tricky to learn ☐ the re☐sults are worth it.

8. There's a mistake in the writing on this report card. Rewrite the part that's wrong, and put the punctuation mark in the right place.

   ....

   ....

   Report Card   Clare Smith

   | Maths B | You've made excellent progress this year — keep up the good work! |
   | French C | Remember to learn the weekly vocab lists (as we discussed in class. |

9. There are **five** mistakes in this paragraph. Circle the **five** punctuation marks that are in the wrong place, then rewrite the paragraph and correct the mistakes.

   > Our army day (Tuesday 16th was) an ordeal. In the, morning we did an obstacle course with, crawl nets climbing walls and mud baths. Jack — my friend looked — awful afterwards. Lunch was alright but the, portions were tiny.

   ....

   ....

   ....

   ....

   ....

Mixed Practice

10. The text below is supposed to be set out in a vertical list with bullet points.
How many bullet points does it need?

a large sheet several chairs some pieces of rope tied into loops a small rug

This list needs .... bullet points.

11. Rewrite each sentence, adding the words and punctuation marks in the boxes in the right places.

Reginald lives in my room. | my pet mouse | — | — |

....

The View Bakery is up for sale. | on Mountain Road | , | , |

....

The zombie invasion was a disaster. | led by Mike | (|) |

....

12. Write a sentence using each set of punctuation marks.

a. .... | (|) |

....

b. .... | — | — |

....

Punctuation Pythons know this section like the back of their... tails. Are you feeling like a Punctuation Python?

Section 3 — Commas, Hyphens, Brackets and Dashes

Colons

Using colons properly is pretty impressive, so get practising with these cool colon questions.

1. Label each of the punctuation marks below with the correct names.

   | ; | | , | | : |

   ....

2. Here are some reasons for using colons. Put a tick after the correct ones.

   • To introduce a list. ☐

   • To join any two sentences. ☐

   • To introduce an explanation. ☐

3. The box below contains three sentences that are jumbled up. Draw a line from the beginning of each sentence to the end, going through the colon in the right place.

   | **Nobody had seen Caleb** | **it's a family heirloom.** | **they were freshly picked.** |

   :   :   :

   | **The teapot is ancient** | **The oranges were tasty** | **he was hiding in the treehouse.** |

4. Rewrite these sentences, adding colons in the correct places.

   The monkeys annoy me they make lots of noise.

   ....

   The sheep are wandering free I forgot to shut the gate.

   ....

Colons

5. Choose three items from the box to complete each sentence.

   Don't forget to use a colon to introduce each list. Only use each word once.

shoes	**blue**	**peas**	**biscuits**	**carrots**
green	**chicken**		**cabbages**	**orange**

   I grow three vegetables ...., ... **and** ....

   The shoes are multicoloured ...., ... **and** ....

   My dog eats three things ...., ... **and** ....

6. Put colons in the correct places so that these sentences make sense.

   We won't be at home ☐ we're going ☐ on holiday ☐ this week.

   The room was full ☐ of people ☐ friends, family ☐ and colleagues.

   Megan is ☐ selling cupcakes ☐ she's raising money ☐ for charity.

   The dog ☐ kept howling during ☐ the thunderstorm ☐ he was so scared.

   I had ☐ three things in my bag ☐ the map, the tickets and ☐ my passport.

7. Tick the sentences which are correct.

   The game was fun: it made me laugh.   ☐

   The bus was blue: the train was green.   ☐

   The king was angry: the people weren't listening.   ☐

   They opened the jam: they boiled the kettle.   ☐

   Remember, a colon introduces an explanation.

Punctuation Pythons laugh in the face of a tricky colon question. Are you a Punctuation Python?

Semicolons

Semicolons can be used to join two complete sentences together.

1. Rewrite these sentences, and replace the conjunction with a semicolon.

    The shop is open **but** there are no carrots left.

    ....

    The journey was uncomfortable **so** I brought a pillow.

    ....

    Pam wants to go to Italy **whereas** Danielle wants to go to Spain.

    ....

2. Circle the sentences below where the underlined
    conjunctions could be replaced with a semicolon.

They usually play rugby <u>but</u> they sometimes play football.	**He filled the fish tank <u>and</u> fed the fish.**
Karim liked maths <u>while</u> at school.	**The rabbit ran quickly <u>yet</u> the fox ran faster.**

3. Add semicolons where they are needed in these lists.

    To make a good cheese sandwich, you need : brown bread, preferably with seeds in it Cheddar cheese that is very strong and lots of butter.

    The best dinosaurs have giant teeth which are as long as fingers green skin, so they can hide in the bushes and long tails to balance.

    At the shop, Tina always buys parsnips, to make parsnip soup ketchup, for ketchup sandwiches and a puzzle book for long bus trips.

Semicolons

4. Put semicolons in the correct places so that these sentences make sense.

The sky is ☐ clear this evening ☐ yesterday ☐ it was cloudy.

I liked ☐ the book ☐ I don't want to see ☐ the film.

Ella is ☐ very determined ☐ she also ☐ loves singing.

He has ☐ a crayon and a pencil ☐ he only uses ☐ the pencil.

My pet snake is called ☐ George ☐ he likes eating ☐ mice.

5. Write in the **four** semicolons that are missing in this passage.

> **Simon likes building towers. He usually makes them out of wooden blocks on special occasions, he makes towers out of other things.**
>
> **The best tower he ever built was made from three packets of biscuits that he took from the jar in the kitchen six bowlfuls of baked beans and his gran's hair curlers.**
>
> **While he was admiring his tremendous tower, Simon's sister raced into the room. The tower got knocked to the ground the whole room was a mess.**

6. Put a tick next to the sentences where semicolons have been used correctly.

We all went to the same school; we've known each other for years. ☐

Steph wrote the letter; she forgot to send it. ☐

My chores include; mowing the lawn, feeding the cat and washing the car. ☐

Today, I want to play squash; go to town with Mum and eat pizza. ☐

I made her a birthday card; at the weekend. ☐

Sssemicolons are sssimple to a Punctuation Python.
How sssimple were these questions for you?   🥚✓ 〰✓ 🐍✓

Section 4 — Colons and Semicolons

Mixed Practice

Let's see how much you know about colons and semicolons with these mixed questions.

1. The box below contains three sentences that are jumbled up. Draw a line from the beginning of each sentence to the end, going through a colon or a semicolon.

> **We bought tickets online**   **He was nervous before the competition**   **it was of her best friends.**
>
> **:**   **;**   **:**
>
> **he really wanted to win.**   **it was a great show.**   **The photograph made her smile**

2. Put a tick next to the sentences that use colons or semicolons correctly.

   Jim rides his horse to school: it's quicker than riding his bike. ☐

   I don't like; wallpaper the carpet is nice. ☐

   We wanted a kitten; we got a goldfish. ☐

   I saw the red dog; a cat, but I'm not sure which one it was; and the raven. ☐

   I love the beach I enjoy swimming; in the sea. ☐

3. Put colons and semicolons in the correct boxes so that these sentences make sense.

   > The man lives ☐ on the Moon ☐ his house is made of ☐ chalk.
   >
   > I always carry ☐ three things ☐ a pen, a lipstick ☐ and a block of cheese.
   >
   > Elsa was watching TV ☐ Sarah ☐ went to school.
   >
   > I bought three flavours of pizza ☐ chicken and mushroom ☐ spinach, tomato and pesto ☐ and ham, cheese and pineapple.

Mixed Practice

4. The punctuation in these sentences is wrong. Rewrite the sentences using colons and semicolons correctly.

There's a surprise in the kitchen for Liz; a new oven.

....

I ate a big lunch; stew, a sandwich and a slice of cake.

....

I like pizza, which is covered in cheese: sausage toasties and chips.

....

....

The soup is made of potatoes, which are from the garden: ham: and eggs.

....

....

5. Write two of your own sentences.

a. Include a **semicolon** and the phrases 'I like' and 'my friend likes'.

....

b. Include a **colon** and an explanation.

....

Punctuation Pythons put pesky punctuation marks in their places. Are you a Punctuation Python?

Section 5 — Mixed Practice

Mixed Practice

Now it's time to test everything you've learnt. Let's see how you do...

1. Using the punctuation marks below, punctuate these sentences correctly.

.	?	!	'	"	,

Julie likes basketball ☐ but she's not very good at it.

Excuse me, can you tell me where the post office is ☐

☐ We need to practise really hard," said Beth.

That's not my hairdryer — it's Georgia ☐ s

Get out of my house or I'll call the police ☐

The Kennedys are going on holiday tomorrow ☐

2. There are **five** mistakes in the use of dashes, colons and semicolons in this paragraph. Circle the mistakes, then rewrite the paragraph correctly so it has four dashes, one colon and one semicolon.

> There's a problem at the bakery; they've run out of flour. Mrs Jenkins — the owner: placed an order for some more, but Mike :her assistant: accidentally cancelled it. Mrs Jenkins doesn't know this: Mike's known about it for weeks.

....

....

....

....

....

Mixed Practice

3. Write down whether each sentence contains a question, a statement or a command, and put a tick after those which include direct speech.

    a. "Do you think we'll arrive on time?" asked Ken. ☐ ....

    b. Caroline can be quite cheeky at times. ☐ ....

    c. Ivy said, "Take the dog for a walk after dinner." ☐ ....

    d. "Come in and sit down!" shouted Mr Frost. ☐ ....

    e. He asked where the baubles had gone. ☐ ....

4. Add the information below to complete these sentences.

    Tomorrow, Lisa and I are going on a trip to ..*Norway*.. │ a country │

    Matthew and .... are best friends. │ a person's name │

    On ...., I'm playing golf. │ a day of the week │

    They are planning to have the wedding in .... │ a month │

    I can't speak .... — it's far too tricky. │ a language │

5. These sentences are missing some punctuation marks.
    Add punctuation marks to the correct boxes.

    That's Tim (from school ☐ **, who is** ☐ **taking part** ☐ **in the play.**

    We had ☐ **better hurry up, or we won** ☐ **t see the** ☐ **beginning.**

    Anne shouted, "Wait for me! ☐ **I want to** ☐ **come too!** ☐

    Wendy, who lives ☐ **next door** ☐ **always bakes** ☐ **really good cakes.**

Mixed Practice

6. Underline the correct words in **bold** in this passage, and put the correct **punctuation mark** in each box.

[ ] (**Don't / Do'nt**) play with my toys! [ ] shouted Kate.

[ ] (**Im / I'm**) not playing with your toys. (**Their / They're**) mine [ ] " Alex replied.

[ ] (**Tha'ts / That's**) not true, [ ] Kate said.

[ ] I (**wouldn't / would'nt**) lie to you, Kate [ ] " replied Alex.

[ ] You lied to me yesterday. (**Did'nt / Didn't**) you [ ] " asked Kate.

[ ] (**I've / Iv'e**) no idea what (**you're / your**) talking about, [ ] Alex said.

7. Complete the sentences below to explain why each punctuation mark has been used.

Julian managed to escape the man-eating shark.

'Man-eating shark' has a hyphen because ....

....

I think Sarah is jealous of Zoe's long hair.

'Zoe's' has an apostrophe because ....

....

She plays golf with her boss, who is also a great rugby player.

This sentence uses a comma because ....

....

Punctuation Pythons are hyssssssterically good at punctuation problems. How good are you?

Proofreading

Proofreading is really handy for checking your work. It's all about reading what you've written and deciding whether you want to make any changes or improvements. You might spot some mistakes too. For these passages, you're just looking for the punctuation and capitalisation errors — there are 15 in each.

1. Draw a circle round the errors. Then rewrite the passage, correcting the mistakes.

> "so, whos next!" asked julie, clutching the microphone and peering into the audience. "Come on, don't be shy. Karaoke is lots of fun."
>
> Andrew turned pale as he watched his mum's hand shoot up in the air like a Rocket. Although she was an ex entertainer (on a european cruise ship, Andrews mum couldnt sing but she thought she had the voice of an angel
>
> "I'll do it?" she shouted, bobbing up and down in her seat. Pick me!"
>
> "No, Mum!" Andrew shouted, tugging at his mum's outstretched arm. "You can't; I'll die of embarrassment. Put your hand down and keep quiet."

....

....

....

....

....

....

....

....

Proofreading

2. There are **15** punctuation errors in this passage. Circle each error, and then rewrite the passage underneath. If you run out of space, use an extra piece of paper to write on.

Something weird was going on at Cheryl's house Tiddles, her cat was burying a bone in the garden. Feathers — her pesky parrot was nibbling on a carrot. Scales her snake) was purring. Rover the dog was talking, and floppy the bunny was hissing.

"What's happened to you all? she asked her pets.

"What's happened to you all?" echoed Rover, flapping his front leg's.

"is every-thing alright," asked Bob as he walked through the door with the Shopping.

"Oh, Bob, I have a whole list of problems; Tiddles thinks he's a dog, Feathers thinks shes a bunny, Scales thinks he's a cat: Rover thinks he's a parrot and Floppy thinks she's a snake. I don't know what to do!" Cheryl cried.

"Right," said Bob, sounding confused. "Shall we call the vet?

....

....

....

....

....

....

....

....

Punctuation Pythons are experts at spotting mistakes.
Did you find all fifteen in each passage? Tick a box.

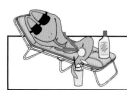

Glossary

COMMON PUNCTUATION MARKS

Apostrophes — show **missing letters** and **belonging**. `,`

Brackets — **separate extra information** in a sentence. `( )`

Bullet points — **separate** different points in a **list**. `•`

Capital letters — used for **proper nouns** and for **starting** sentences. `A`

Colons — **introduce some lists** and **join sentences**. `:`

Commas — **separate** items in a **list**, separate **extra information** in a sentence and **join clauses**. `,`

Dashes — **separate extra information** in a sentence. `—`

Exclamation marks — show **strong feeling** or **commands**. `!`

Full stops — show where sentences end. `.`

Hyphens — **link words** or parts of words to make the meaning clear. `-`

Inverted commas show **direct speech**. `" "`

Question marks — used at the **end** of **questions**. `?`

Semicolons — **separate lists** of **longer things** and **join sentences**. `;`

USEFUL WORDS

Command — A **sentence** that **tells** somebody to **do something**.

Direct speech — The **actual words** that are **said** by someone.

Proper noun — A **noun** that is the **name** of a **specific person**, **place** or **thing**.

Question — A **sentence** that **asks something**.

Reported speech — What someone has said, but **not in their own words**.

Statement — A **sentence** that **gives information**.

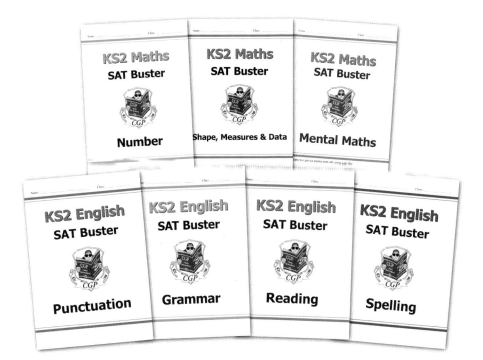